Lizzy's triumph over cyber-bullying!

Nina Du Thaler

Hi, my name is Elle.

I'm just an ordinary kid. I'm not sure what I'm going to be when I grow up but I'm sure I'm destined for greatness.

I always wonder about growing up. I wish I could grow up faster. Whenever I ask a grown-up if I can do something new, they give me a strange look and say, "Don't wish your childhood away!" or "Maybe when you're a little older." I wonder when that day will come because I am older each day than I was the day before!

What's interesting about me? Hmmm, let me think...

When I was little I found my name very confusing. First, I learned about the letters of the alphabet and for a long time I thought my name was spelled "L". Then, I learned it was actually "E" "L" "L" "E". Very weird! It has sort of stuck now and I sign cards and letters "L".

I've made a shocking discovery that I don't know much about cyber-safety. In fact, I don't even know what cyber-safety means. How embarrassing!

I'm sharing my diary and what I've learned with you to save you this embarrassment.

Cyber-safety is all about how to safely use the Internet, computers, mobile phones, tablets and other cool gadgets.

I also have a totally cool group of friends who are going to help us with this. Together, we will explore the cyber-world so you don't have to make any of our mistakes.

Let me introduce my friends …

I am ... Lizzy, always happy and singing and try to see the bright side of things
I Think ... Elle is my BFF (Best Friend Forever)

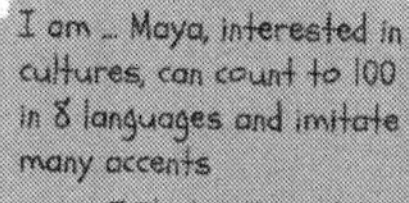
I am ... Maya, interested in cultures, can count to 100 in 8 languages and imitate many accents
I Think ... I want to be a librarian

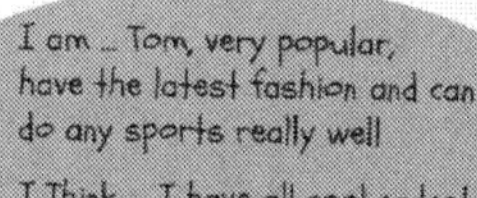
I am ... Tom, very popular, have the latest fashion and can do any sports really well
I Think..... I have all cool gadgets there are
OK

12-21-3-25

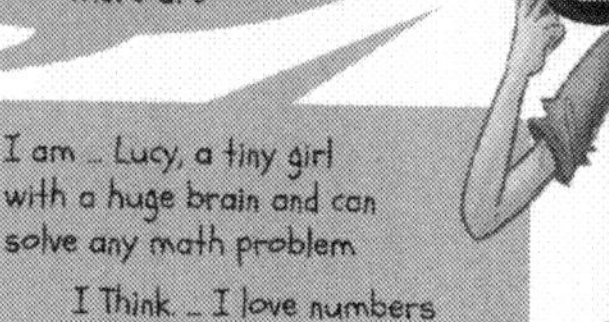
I am ... Lucy, a tiny girl with a huge brain and can solve any math problem
I Think. ... I love numbers more than anything

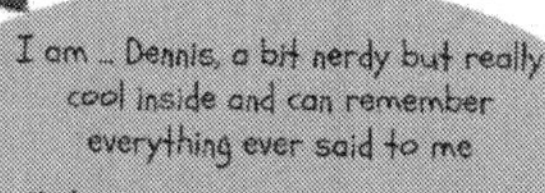
I am ... Dennis, a bit nerdy but really cool inside and can remember everything ever said to me
I Think ... I can beat Tom running one day

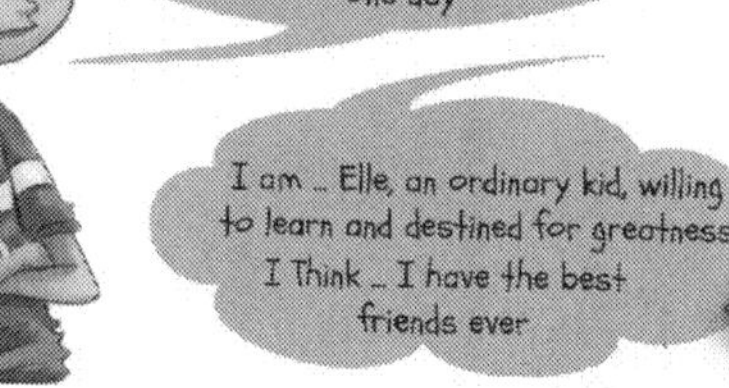
I am ... Elle, an ordinary kid, willing to learn and destined for greatness
I Think ... I have the best friends ever

Wednesday

Sleepover invitation, Spanish accent, acting strange!

So far, it's been a long, long week.

I was sitting on a beach. I could hear the swoosh, swoosh, swoosh of the waves landing on the sand. I couldn't believe my eyes. All around me were mermaids swimming in the blue waters of the ocean. Splish, splash, giggle, giggle, chatter, chatter! I could just hear the sounds of their voices over the continuously crashing waves. Mermaids were bobbing up and down with the rhythm of the waves, some sneakily waving to me while another one of the mermaids flicked some water at me – splash!

I couldn't quite work out what had happened. Why was my face wet?

I looked around and realised that I had been daydreaming. I was sitting under a tree in the playground and not on a beach at all.

I looked up to see the smiling and sneaky face of one of my friends – Maya.

"Gotcha!" she said, putting her water bottle back in her bag.

As always, I was stunned by Maya's piercing light blue eyes that contrasted against her dark skin and curly dark brown hair. She held a huge hardback book almost the same size as her schoolbag in her hand.

"Hey!" I exclaimed.

I gathered my thoughts as Maya started talking at her usual fast pace.

Jibber, jabber, jibber, jabber ...

"... about my sleepover. I'm so totally excited because Saturday is soooo close. Dad is putting up tents in the garden so we'll be able to have fun without the grown-ups watching over us," said Maya in a Spanish accent. "We might even get to see the lunar eclipse if the sky is clear," she continued, waving the huge book about astronomy in front of me.

Maya is always talking in weird and quirky accents, and pretending to be different people. Today was obviously Spanish day. She is always reading and learns a lot about anything she puts her mind to. Today her topic appeared to be the moon, but I didn't have time to worry about it right now. To be totally honest, I wasn't interested in astronomy, or the moon, or any lunar ellipse but wanted to find out about the sleepover.

"Who's coming?" I asked.

"Well, this year is really special because Ben and I are turning ten - double digits! Just like you did. Dad is setting up a boys' tent and a girls' tent," she replied.

"Ew, boy's germs," I said. Even though some of my friends were boys, it was still funny to joke about boy's germs.

"Don't worry. The boys will be far enough away that we won't get boy germs," she said with a screwed-up face to match the one I had just pulled.

Maya and Ben (or Benjamin) are twins. Maya refers to him as her younger brother even though he was born only twenty-nine minutes after her on the exact same day. Sometimes Ben just accepts her annoying comments; other times he gets more than a little upset. I think Maya secretly enjoys annoying him and watching him react!

"Lots of my friends are coming, including Lucy and Lizzy," she replied.

Elizabeth, or Lizzy, is my best friend. We share everything – lunches, clothes, homework answers (not that we would ever admit it to our teacher), thoughts, silly songs and even a secret handshake.

I couldn't wait to see Lizzy to talk to her about the sleepover. However, when I got to class, Lizzy wasn't there. I asked Mrs Hudson if she had seen Lizzy, and she replied that Lizzy was sick.

That's strange, Lizzy has been sick four times recently and that's not like Lizzy. I know she hates being sick and missing out on school, I thought.

Recently, I had been thinking that Lizzy and I seemed to be drifting apart. It was almost like Lizzy was avoiding me, and I was beginning to wonder if I had done something to hurt her feelings. Over the past few days, I hadn't seen Lizzy much and when I did she appeared to be quiet and a little sad.

I'll ring her when I get home because my mobile phone is only for important calls during the day – she always loves chatting on the phone after school, I thought.

When I returned home later in the day, I rang to talk to Lizzy but her mother said she was sick and didn't want to talk to anyone.

Weird, I thought.

I mentioned it to Mum. She said it was probably nothing, but I was worried.

Friday

Scary stories!

I was late joining my group of friends for lunch, because I had stopped at the canteen to pick up lunch on my way back from art class. As I approached my group of friends I could see they were sitting in a close circle all leaning in towards Dennis, listening to his every word and concentrating on what he was saying.

Dennis has always been the storyteller in our group, and he takes great delight in scaring the socks off us with his stories.

I wondered what was so interesting, but as I got closer I could tell by looks on their faces that it was a scary story.

I sat down in the group and began to listen to his story.

"... because I was scared by all the weird sounds inside the house I decided that I would wait on the porch.

"I walked out the front door and then remembered that my mobile phone was still inside. I turned to go back inside and get it. Bang! The door slammed in my face. What was I going to do? I was locked out. And, worst of all, I didn't have my mobile phone with me.

"I crept around the outside of the house, hoping to find an open window or door. Not that I really wanted to go back inside with all those weird scary sounds. No luck! To-wit-to-woo! To-wit-to-woo! Rustle, rustle. What was that?

"At this point, I was considering whether I would be less scared inside the house with the weird sounds or outside in the dark with the scary animals.

"Until my friend arrived to join me, I was alone in this dark, spooky forest. To-wit-to-woo! Screech. To-wit-to-woo! Creak, creak. Then, I thought I heard someone calling my name. Thinking it might be my friend, I walked cautiously out into the spooky forest.

"It was so, so dark with just slivers of light from the moon above coming through the trees. There were spooky shadows jumping out at me at every turn. To-wit-to-woo! Screech! Bang, creak, rustle, drip. I was really afraid of every sound.

"Shadows, more shadows, big dark shadows, long deep shadows, shadows that seemed to reach for me … The branches and leaves on the trees looked like arms and hands reaching for me. I was scared and just wanted to get out of there.

"There were owls, rats, bats, moths, spiders and all sorts of creatures circling around me. To-wit-to-woo! Creak, rustle. To-wit-to-woo! Bang, drip, rustle. All the weird animal calls were getting louder and closer.

"I turned back towards the house. I heard a screech overhead and looked up to see a bat flying straight towards me. I ducked down quickly but lost my footing. When I got back up I was confused and couldn't work out which was the way back to the house. I looked around and could only see shadows and darkness.

"I was lost.

"My legs were shaking. Not little quivers but great big shakes that almost made my knees knock together. Goose bumps slowly crawled up my neck and into my hair from my back and arms. In fact my whole body was cold and quivering.

"Then, I saw a shadow out of the corner of my eye. It was big and almost as long as me.

"'W-w-who is there? W-w-what do you want?' I stammered.

"There was no answer. But I didn't need to hear an answer. I ran like crazy back towards the house. No, no wait – other way! I ran and ran but the shadow was chasing me. It was right behind me, following me and breathing down my neck the whole time.

"Then, I stumbled on something lying on the ground and fell over. I was lying face down on my stomach, scared out of my mind, with my hands over my head when I realised …

"I had been running from my own shadow."

"Oh Dennis, you gave me goose bumps with that story," said Maya.

"It wasn't that scary. In fact, I found it boring," snapped Lizzy as she got up and walked away.

Maya and I exchanged questioning glances.

I was surprised by this outburst from Lizzy. She was normally such a happy and kind person and would never say anything mean to anyone, let alone anyone in our close-knit group.

Why is Lizzy acting so badly? I wondered.

Brrriiinnnggg! The end-of-lunch bell rang and interrupted my thoughts. I had to move to my classroom quickly before Mrs Hudson started the class.

Mrs Hudson is my favourite teacher. She is tall and skinny with dark brown, almost-black hair that she always wears in a tight bun on the top of her head like a ballerina.

I often wondered whether she did ballet when she was younger.

We were asked to work on an English activity in the computer lab. We each have a login to e-classroom - our classroom online environment. I love working in e-classroom because it allows my class to send messages to each other, share files and photos, and work together on assignments and activities. It's really cool.

Mrs Hudson says it is a safe online place for us to come together as a class and practise our online skills as well before we enter the world of the Internet.

Lizzy and I send messages back and forth to each other all the time. Lizzy sits a couple of seats across from me, and I can tell if she is thinking because she hums a little tune. But today, there was no humming and when I turned around to glance at Lizzy, she looked miserable. She seemed to be upset with her computer - tapping hard on her keyboard and getting really frustrated.

I sent her a happy message (even included a smiley face in it!) to try and cheer her up, but she didn't respond.

After class I asked her if there was a problem with her computer, but she didn't really answer. She mumbled that she had to get back to the classroom and wandered off a bit distracted.

I had to get to the bottom of what was worrying her.

Saturday and Sunday

Get ready; it's the sleepover!

It was 6.30 am Saturday morning and I was wide awake. The alarm hadn't gone off because I don't set it for Saturdays – I much prefer to wake up slowly.

Normally I go to swimming lessons on Saturday, but today was very different. I was excited because I was going to the sleepover at Maya and Ben's. I was practically jumping out of my skin with anticipation. I was also really, really hungry and my tummy (as always) was grumbling.

Of course, I had been to sleepovers before, but this one was going to be different. We were all going to be sleeping (if we actually slept) in tents in the garden. I loved the thought of how creepy and scary this would be. The creepy stories the boys had been talking about over the last few days had really freaked me out, not that I was going to admit that to any of my friends. We were going to be totally on our own with no parents to tell us what to do.

There were eight girls going (not sure how many boys – who cares anyway!) and we all had to take sleeping bags with us. How exciting!

While Dad had a shower, shaved and grumbled about getting up so early on a Saturday, I packed, repacked and then checked and rechecked my bag, then changed bags for a slightly bigger one. Okay, I was nervous and packing and checking somehow helped me deal with my nervousness. As well as all the things I needed, I packed some sneaky treats for later that night, as well as the gift.

Mum was buzzing around the house, trying to tidy up before we left.

It was nearly 9 am, and I was getting really impatient when Dad finally appeared in the kitchen.

"Are you sure you've packed everything you need?" Dad asked.

"Yep, let's go," I replied.

"Gift, swimmers, clean clothes for tomorrow, underwear?" Mum asked.

"Oh, Mum!" I replied embarrassed that she was asking me about my underwear in front of Dad. Ew!

"What about your sleeping bag?" she asked persisting with her checklist.

"Yep, just here. Dad, can you carry it to the car, please?" I asked.

I climbed into the front seat of the car after throwing my bag on the rear seat. Dad climbed into the driver's seat and started the car. I jumped out of my seat when the radio blasted into action at a high volume. This happens quite often after Dad has driven home from work by himself. He must turn up the music and sing along while driving home. Must look quite funny from outside the car. Parents can be so embarrassing sometimes, and they don't seem to get it!

Five minutes later, I stood in front of a large apple-green door and rang the doorbell - ding dong, ding dong ...

The door opened to a flurry of movement and laughter. All our friends were there, excitedly bouncing around.

I grabbed the sleeping bag from Dad and waved goodbye. I wasn't going to kiss him in front of my friends - bleck! Luckily for me he seemed to understand how our relationship worked and waved goodbye and headed back to his car.

"Let the party begin," shouted Maya.

We all raced through the house and outside to set up in our new home - the tent. Both tents - the girls' palace and the boys' castle - were already constructed in the garden, complete with a red carpet leading down to the girls' palace and a stone-edged path leading to the bottom of the garden where the boys' tent was set up. There were flowering plants in pots placed either side of the entrance to the girls' tent.

Quite posh, I thought.

Then without so much as a second to think, a flurry of activity commenced. The gifts were pushed to one side as we excitedly dropped our bags and started unfurling our sleeping bags. There were some minor arguments, many rearrangements and then group satisfaction while each of us worked out who we wanted next to us.

Being my bestie, Lizzy was next to me. I looked across at her and expected to see her smiling happy face, but that didn't seem to be the case. For a moment, I felt her sadness but it was hard to be sad for very long with all my other friends around and the activities of the party going on.

Perhaps Lizzy is just a little tired? I thought.

The sleepover continued into the afternoon with the opening of the gifts, watching a couple of movies, dancing to popular songs and eating too much party food. A couple of times, I noticed Lizzy checking her mobile phone. It looked like she was at the party but not really there and not really enjoying herself. I wondered if something had happened at home.

Finally, it was time to settle into our sleeping bags and go to sleep. I realised that we had completely missed the eclipse because we were having too much fun. After cleaning our teeth, we all climbed into our sleeping bags and turned off the light that Maya's dad had set up in the tent. Even though Maya's parents had told us to go to sleep, many of the girls told scary stories; the others giggled and laughed at different silly stories, and there was not really any sleeping being done.

After a few moments, I could hear Lizzy sobbing quietly. Luckily the other girls couldn't hear because of the giggling and silly noises. I was concerned and moved over closer to her.

"What's wrong, Lizzy?" I whispered.

She didn't reply and tried to disguise her sobs by sniffing like she had a blocked nose.

"Lizzy, I can tell you're not happy. Do you miss sleeping in your own bedroom?" I whispered.

Again, she didn't reply. I was beginning to get really worried. I moved closer to her so that I could hug her. She was quiet for the rest of the night and drifted off to sleep.

As I fell asleep I wondered what was upsetting my best friend and how I could get her to share her problem with me.

Early Sunday morning I woke up and immediately remembered that I still didn't know what was wrong with Lizzy. My brain hadn't come up with any solutions in my sleep.

She wasn't even in the tent.

All the other girls were still asleep, so I carefully wobbled and tiptoed in between sleeping bags, over sleeping bodies and all manner of clothes spread randomly around the tent.

I found Lizzy sitting in one of the garden lounges overlooking the pool.

"Hey," I said.

"Hey," she replied looking at me with half a smile.

After a few moments of general chit-chat, I told her that I was troubled because she didn't seem happy.

"Have I done something to hurt your feelings?" I asked.

"I don't want to talk about it," she snapped and walked off.

I couldn't work out how to get through to her. I was really concerned that for the first time ever she wouldn't tell me what was wrong. It had to be something I had done.

I need to ask someone about how to get Lizzy to share with me what is wrong. I can't fix it if she doesn't tell me, I thought.

Monday

Mrs Hudson and my plan!

Back at school, I couldn't concentrate on my schoolwork because I was more worried than ever about Lizzy.

Mrs Hudson was explaining, "… so if we divide by 5 … then we get 5 groups of 20 … okay, let's try that again …"

The more I tried to concentrate the more my brain focused on what I might have done to hurt Lizzy's feelings. Thinking, thinking, worry, worry, worry!

Then, crash, some of my books and pencils dropped on the floor. Everyone was looking at me wondering what had happened. Mrs Hudson looked at me in a questioning way and asked me something. I realised that I didn't have a clue what she was asking. My brain was … scrambling, worrying … worrying … worrying!

Mrs Hudson continued on with the lesson, leaving me to recover my things from the floor.

I could ask her what she would do about this whole Lizzy thing, I thought.

Mrs Hudson was always willing to listen and good at solving problems.

I remembered when Mrs Hudson had resolved a disagreement between two of the girls in my class. She listened to each of the girls in turn and then sat them both down and asked them to explain their different points of view. When they had each done this, she asked them to think about how they could solve this problem by supporting and understanding each other rather than arguing.

After class, as slowly as I could, I packed up my books and placed them in my bag. As I had planned, by the time I had finished packing my things away, the rest of the class had left. I nervously stood in front of Mrs Hudson.

"Did you want to see me?" she asked.

I hesitated for a moment, wondering whether I should waste her time on such a small issue. Mrs Hudson pulled a chair around next to her for me to sit in. I still wondered whether Mrs Hudson would think I was wasting her time by asking about friendship problems but she seemed eager to help me.

I fumbled and fidgeted for a while, not sure how to start telling her about what was going on.

She grabbed a cup full of coloured pens and pencils and started drawing on a piece of blank paper. I wondered what she was doing - weird!

Before I knew what I was doing, I had sat down on the seat and started drawing with her. Then I realised I had spent a few minutes talking about Lizzy and how she had been acting. I said that I was worried that I had done something to hurt Lizzy's feelings. I was worried because Lizzy had been away from school even though she loved school, was quiet and sad, and was snapping at all her friends. And, I asked her how I could get Lizzy to share her problems with me.

We talked and talked. Phew! I felt so much better having shared my worries.

"Sometimes it's hard to talk about problems. Perhaps you could get her to write it down," Mrs Hudson suggested.

"That's a brilliant idea," I said.

After school, I texted Lizzy, as I quite often do. This time, however, I had a plan. Tap, tap, tap on the phone keypad ... My plan slowly came together.

As I climbed into bed, I wished that tomorrow would be a better day for Lizzy and I, but I wasn't sure my plan would work.

Tuesday

Suddenly it all makes sense!

To my total surprise, when I opened my school locker, there was a bright white envelope that had been posted through one of the vent holes. It had my name neatly written on the front and was from Lizzy – I could tell by the writing. I tucked it under my arm and headed to a quiet spot to read Lizzy's letter.

As I read her letter, I was aghast at what Lizzy had written. My chin dropped and my mouth fell open in shock. I was speechless (not something that happens very often!). My eyes skimmed across her words as quickly as they could, but I was reading so fast I had to re-read parts of her letter over and over. Slowly tears formed in my eyes and rolled down my cheeks. I suddenly understood what had been happening and realised just how miserable she must be feeling.

Lizzy wrote about how she loved computers and, having a mobile phone, she loved sending messages to me and our other friends, but then suddenly everything changed for her. She wrote about how sad, alone and embarrassed she felt about what was happening and how she felt no-one would understand or be able to help her.

"Someone broke into my school email account and has been pretending to be me," she wrote.

She explained that someone had been sending embarrassing messages to some of her friends. Someone else had sent her an email asking about whether she thought one of the boys in her class was cute. When she replied that he was cute, they posted her answer on e-classroom.

"I thought it was an email from you, Elle. That's why I shared my private thoughts," she wrote.

She received a very official email telling her that she wasn't allowed to be a member of her gymnastics club online chat room because some of the messages she had posted were rude and against the rules of conduct. But these weren't her messages.

"The girls from gymnastics have 'unfriended' me in e-classroom. I feel really left out because they use it as well as email and mobile phone messages to share stories, talk about what we did in class and invite each other to parties," she wrote.

Bing! My brain fired into action. Suddenly, a really strange email I had received from Lizzy last week made sense … It wasn't her at all!

"I've also been getting a lot of unwanted messages on my mobile phone. I don't even know who they're coming from, but they're so mean," she wrote.

"I don't know who it is or what to do about it. I've realised that I didn't share this with you, and you tried so hard to help me. Please forgive me and help me now," wrote Lizzy.

After reading her letter, I felt so sad and so relieved at the same time – sad because of what had been happening to Lizzy and relieved because it was nothing that I had done.

I felt so bad as well. Why didn't I notice what was happening? What sort of a best friend was I? How could I help her now?

I thought about it for a while. Bing, bing! My brain fired into action again. Tick, tick, tick! I had a plan!

When I got home I texted Lizzy.

Lizzy texted back.

That night I climbed into bed and I slept like a log, knowing that together Lizzy and I could solve any problem.

Wednesday

It's called cyber-bullying!

As I waited for Lizzy to get to school, I thought about all the challenges we had lived through together and all the problems we had solved together. We are a good duo.

As Lizzy walked towards me, I could see tears rolling down her cheeks. Then tears started rolling down my cheeks. Sniff, sniff, sniff. We hugged each other for a long time. Sniff, sniff, sniff. There was no need for words … We each knew what the other was thinking and feeling. We were back together. The duo – stronger than ever!

Mr Nile opened the library doors. He had a typical librarian look about him – black-rimmed glasses, white long-sleeved shirt neatly tucked into his navy trousers, super shiny black leather shoes and not a hair out of place. We zigzagged past him, almost knocking him over, and up to the computer lab. We quickly located a computer to search the Internet and pulled two chairs together so we could share the computer. Lizzy appeared very nervous about using the computer.

"We're just going to research what to do," I reassured her.

We had learned about searching the Internet in class. After a few moments of surfing the Internet, I found a site that explained some of the things that we could try.

"Look, Lizzy, it says what has been happening to you is called cyber-bullying," I whispered excitedly. (After all, it was the library.)

She scooted her chair a little closer and read out the large text at the top of the page we had found. "Cyber-bullying is bullying that is done to hurt or embarrass someone using technology, such as the Internet, a mobile phone or a camera."

"But how do we stop it?" she asked.

I read on and found a list of things to do. I read them out loud and copied some down in my notebook.

- Always tell someone you trust about what is happening if you are not comfortable.
- Don't answer any of the bullying messages. Save them and show them to someone you trust.

- Get someone you trust to help you block anyone you don't want contacting you so they can't contact you anymore.
- Log out and don't use the online service until you have someone help you set up new accounts.
- Find out how to report bullying on the online services that you are using.
- Report the bully to the administrator, game or video host so they get blocked.

"It says here sometimes when you first tell someone you trust, they don't think it is a big deal and they might not listen to you. So you have to keep telling them until they listen and help," I read to her from the Internet page.

"Who do you think they mean by someone you trust?" asked Lizzy.

"Let's make a list. I would add Mum, Dad, my brother and sister, my Grandma …" I replied.

"Add our teachers, uncles and aunts, a family friend," she butted in.

Later that day, we were wandering around the sports field, just chatting and catching up, when we bumped into Jack.

He is one athletic dude - he has super long, powerful legs, long arms that seem to go on forever, and he's always dressed in something sporty that has his name on the back.

We were supposed to be running around the track practising our athletic drills, but Lizzy and I had slowed to a walk. Our teacher didn't seem to mind as long as we were still moving.

Jack was practising his long jump. Run, run, run, run, huummpp! Jump, splat, ouch! He was my friend Tom's older brother, and I knew I could talk to him when I wanted help and advice.

I gave Lizzy a look to say "trust me" as I started to explain to him what had happened. As he stretched his muscles and listened closely to our story, Lizzy became more confident and chimed in with parts of the story. I think it helped her to talk some more about what had happened and how she had felt.

After Jack listened to our story and answered our many questions, I could see that Lizzy was feeling relieved and more convinced that we could deal with this situation.

"If someone is being mean to you while you are on the Internet or on your mobile phone, you should always talk to someone you trust about it," he said.

Hmmm, he's smart; that's just what the Internet said, I thought.

"I feel really embarrassed though," Lizzy replied.

Jack made her promise to tell her parents about what had happened, and he made me promise to go with Lizzy to support her.

"Remember it isn't your fault if someone is bullying you online. Nobody should be bullied," he said as he raced off with all his effort down the long-jump path.

Friday

Important friend business to take care of!

Friday: last day of the school week - yee-hah!

I slid out of bed, gradually exposing my body to the cool air outside my nice warm cocoon. I decided to wear a tracksuit today - school uniform of course!

I had a devious thought as I was putting on my socks. *No-one will notice if I don't wear school uniform socks. Chuckle, chuckle - no-one would notice if I wear completely odd socks.*

And so, I pulled my school uniform sock off my foot, rummaged through my sock basket and started my day with a crazy decision to wear one yellow and one orange sock to school.

During the drive to school, I told Mum about what had been happening to Lizzy and asked if I could walk home with her to her house.

"Really important friend business to take care of," I told her.

I could tell she was proud by the look she gave me, and it felt good.

Mum said she would pick me up from Lizzy's house later in the afternoon. And with that, she drew to a stop a block away from the school and I exited the car. Standing on the path, I made a heart shape with both of my hands by arching my fingers and pushing my wrists together, and then I pointed at her. Our secret way of saying I love you. Shhh, don't tell anyone!

My day was crazy busy – a trip to the library, morning tea, buying lunch at the school canteen, a couple of games of handball. And as quickly as it had started, it was over.

After school I met Lizzy under the big tree, and then we strolled home together. I could tell she was super nervous because she hardly spoke a word the whole trip. Secretly, I didn't mind because I had so much to talk about. I talked and talked and talked, only stopping for the occasional "uh-huh" from Lizzy.

When we arrived at Lizzy's house her parents were both home. Her father works from home some days doing "strategic planning". I have no idea what that means, but he says it is very important! Today, he had littered the living room floor with huge sheets of paper covered with different-coloured sticky notes and large writing.

While Lizzy's mum flitted back and forth between the laundry and the kitchen, dodging the huge sheets of paper, doing the washing and putting away plates, Lizzy lingered and fidgeted. I gave her the "just tell them you want to speak to them" look.

She finally blurted out, "Mum, I need to have a conversation with you and Dad about something."

Woah, "conversation". That sounds serious, I thought.

We all sat down at the table in their kitchen - after all, there was no room in the living room. Both of her parents had really worried looks on their faces. Lizzy opened her mouth to start talking, but she couldn't. Tears quickly welled up in her eyes and rolled down her face.

I moved closer to Lizzy, put my arm around her and started telling her story. I talked about what had been happening and finished by saying, "Cyber-bullying. That's what it's called!"

"How did I get myself into such a mess? I feel so embarrassed and scared," she sobbed.

We mentioned the trusted friend, Jack, we had talked to, the research we had done and what we had found out.

I think Lizzy's parents were really shocked at first, but then they asked lots of questions about what had been happening. Her dad mentioned that similar things had happened in his workplace. Lizzy admitted to her parents that she was scared to talk to them about this. They understood and comforted Lizzy.

"What did you use as your password, Lizzy?" enquired her Dad.

"Elle," she replied.

Awkward, I thought.

"That is what we call a weak password – something that someone else could easily guess," he explained. "You should create a strong password that uses a secret word, a number and a special character, and never respond to any of the nasty texts or comments."

Together, Lizzy, her mum and I created and wrote down a new strong password for her to use. While we were doing that, her father changed the settings on her mobile phone to block some of the numbers that Lizzy was receiving nasty texts from.

"We might need to close down some of your online accounts as well," said her dad.

"But ...?" began Lizzy, concerned that she might lose all of her online friends.

"We'll create new online accounts for you using your new secure password. Everything will be okay. Trust me," he said with a knowing smile.

"We can also check the privacy options on your social networking sites," her mum commented.

Wow, I didn't know parents could know so much about this stuff, I thought.

"I'm really impressed with the research you have done and what you have found out by yourselves. Why don't you ask your teacher if you can share it with the class?" he asked.

"Good idea," I chimed in.

I could tell that Lizzy felt happy, brave and somehow more capable of handling the situation than yesterday.

I made an entry in my notebook about creating a good password.

Afterwards, her parents seemed relieved. *I don't know what they were thinking we were going to talk about? Getting in trouble at school, boys – eeek!* I thought.

Saturday

Happier times!

I love Saturdays.

Lizzy and I were back at swimming this week, but the water seemed so much colder after having a week off for the sleepover. The weather was definitely getting cooler, but surely winter couldn't be that close!

There isn't much time for talking though, because our swimming teacher keeps us busy swimming up and down the lanes - freestyle, backstroke, breaststroke, diving and tumble turns. Lizzy and I sometimes try to yell to each other under the water, but it just comes out as a garbled sound.

"Practise, practise, practise," our swimming teacher always reminds us.

Today is a super exciting day though, because we are invited to SK8TER - a skateboard and scooter park - for a party for one of the other kids in my class. Parties, parties, parties - the life of a social ten-year-old. Pretty awesome and totally cool, hey? Although, I must admit, I will be happy to have a quiet and relaxing weekend next weekend.

The skateboard and scooter park had lots of places for us to explore.

Lizzy and I were scooting around the park, in and out, between other kids, when we heard an announcement.

"Group B, please line up at the start line for your race," boomed the speakers.

"That's us," I yelled at Lizzy over the noise.

We all lined up for the race and jostled for the best position at the start line. A few of the boys were on skateboards and a few had scooters. Most of the girls had scooters. The boys' scooters were all banged up and mean looking with skulls, bones and scary pictures, while the girls' scooters seemed to have glitter on them that sparkled in the sunlight.

"On your mark, get set, gooooo!" boomed the speakers.

And we were off ... There were kids, skateboards and scooters everywhere. A sea of wheels, knee pads, helmets and sneakers pushing off the ground followed by a chorus of excited yells, high-pitched squeals, panting and heavy breathing. I must admit it was quite a sight!

I took off with the rest of the group, but before long I was trailing one or two other kids.

The race was a bit of an obstacle course - down a hill, across a narrow bridge, through a tunnel ... Push, push, push. I was so proud of myself because I hadn't fallen off and I wasn't tired at all.

Then, my legs started to feel heavy and exhausted, and I couldn't see the finish line in sight. Phew, now I felt tired!

After a while I saw a sign that said "Halfway" and wondered if I would ever make it to the end. Grrr, push, push, push ...

On both sides of the obstacle course, kids and grown-ups were shouting and cheering us on.

I looked across at Lizzy who had kept pace with me. She was smiling from one ear to the other. She gave me the thumbs up and then accelerated past me with an extra-hard push.

"See ya," she yelled.

I felt like a real athlete with everyone watching and cheering. Then I caught a glimpse of Lizzy's mum and my mum standing on the side of the course near the finish line. My mum was holding her mobile phone up in front of her. I pushed an annoying, dangling piece of hair out of my eyes, straightened up and pushed my shoulders back in case she was going to take a photo. You can never look too good in a photo!

At last Lizzy and I crossed the finish line, jumped off our scooters, hugged each other and fell to the ground.

Being a kid is so much work!

Monday

It's so nice for our group to be back to normal!

For the first time in over a week, our group of friends were all sitting together for lunch, and Lizzy was obviously happy.

Tom opened his lunch box.

"Oh man, phew! This must be Friday's lunch. I must have forgotten to take it out of my bag," said Tom.

"Mum always says it is my 'responsibility' to clean out my lunch box and prepare it for the next day," I commented.

"Ditto," he said.

There were ants everywhere, crawling all over the food in the lunch box. It was like he had awakened an army of ants. Stomp, stomp, stomp, munch, munch, munch! They marched out of the lunch box and up his arms. He flicked his arms as if doing a weird dance to try and get rid of them, but they were everywhere. Each ant was intent on carrying their piece of stinky food from the lunch box to their home via his body.

My stomach heaved from the smell and the thought of ants all over my body.

Did I tell you I hate ants? In fact I hate all creepy, crawly things. I am even afraid of ladybugs … yes, little, iddy, biddy ladybugs! I know it's so embarrassing, but I can't control it.

Tom ran with the lunch box containing the exploding ants' nest to the rubbish bin and dropped the whole lunch box into the bin. While he danced around trying to flick the remaining ants off, I wondered what his mum would say about him throwing away his lunch box. Probably nothing – they were rich beyond rich!

We all laughed at Tom – big belly laughs.

* * *

Lizzy had learned a lot over the past few weeks. She had even shared her experience with our class.

Lizzy had stopped receiving nasty texts and phone calls. Even though her cyber-bullying problems weren't completely over, she felt so much better for sharing her story and rallying support from friends and family.

I checked my notebook for the list of things to do if you are cyber-bullied:

- Always, always, always tell someone you trust about what is happening if you are not comfortable.
- Don't answer any of the bullying messages. Save them and show them to someone you trust.
- Get someone you trust to help you block anyone you don't want contacting you so they can't contact you anymore.
- Log out and create new accounts for your online services.
- Check the privacy options on your social networking sites.
- Find out how to report cyber-bullying to the online services that you are using and report the bully so they get blocked.
- Create a good, strong password that contains a secret word, a number and a special character.
- Close down any accounts that have been used by someone without your permission and open new ones.

I added one final thought to my list:

- Think before you send any message. Don't send anything you wouldn't like to receive yourself.

It is so nice for our group to be back to normal, I thought to myself.

I had learned so much from Lizzy's painful experience.

I am not perfect but I think I'm pretty close to it, and I'm always willing to learn!

Remember, you might not believe it, but there's always someone you can go to for help, and it's never too late.

Dear friends

Although a diary is private, I'm happy to share mine with you. I hope you enjoyed learning from my cyber-adventure.

Watch out for my next book. I'm sure it will rock your socks off and be another exciting cyber-journey.

Until next time, be safe when using and playing with technology.

Thanks for reading.

L

P.S. Thank you very much for reading my book! I hope you liked it.

I know your time is valuable. However, please take a brief moment to leave a review and I will appreciate it.

Your effort will assist new readers find my work, decide if the book is for them and help me with my future writing.

Thank you again, and be sure to keep a look out for the next book in my Diary of Elle series!

P.P.S. Want to find out more about me and my friends, please visit my website www.diaryofelle.com.

About the Series

The series, Diary of Elle, informs and inspires children's awareness of cyber-safety through fun stories in diary-format. Starring Elle (the diary-owner) and her friends, each book in the series of seven books will allow children to learn about a different cyber-safety concept through the experiences of other children.

About the Author

Nina Du Thaler began working in the Information Technology (IT) industry long before authoring her first book. She is also a mother of a 9 year old daughter (almost double digits!) and works as a Chief Information Officer (CIO), responsible for the IT environment within a large company in Australia.

She has experienced first hand the positive and negative impacts that technology can have on children's daily lives. It is pervasive and they use it easily and without hesitation, but they are unaware of potential consequences and we have not equipped our children to have the skills to deal with these challenges.

In the series, Diary of Elle, she combines her knowledge and experience in IT and parenthood, into a unique combination of fun products (featuring Elle and her friends), so that children can learn from other children's experiences.

Nina and Elle wish you fun reading, with some learning on the side!

Copyright Notice

Lizzy's Triumph Over Cyber-bullying!
by Nina Du Thaler

ISBN: 978-1-925300-04-8

First published January 2015 by Bright Zebra Pty Ltd.

Cover and illustrations by Fanny Liem
Edited by Helena Newton, The Expert Editor

Special thanks to Bob Beusekom, Merrilea Charles, Kylee Williamson and Natia Meyers :-)

Made in the USA
Middletown, DE
21 April 2023